Ned Rorem
Piano Album II

BOOSEY & HAWKES

DISTRIBUTED BY

HAL•LEONARD®
CORPORATION
7777 W. BLUEMOUND RD. P.O. BOX 13819 MILWAUKEE, WI 53213

www.boosey.com
www.halleonard.com

COMPOSER'S NOTE

Recalling

Since non-vocal music cannot be proved to have literary meaning, but since my nature is oral as well as aural, I like to adorn my abstract work with concrete titles. Hence the names for the three sections of *Recalling*, a suite specifically tailored to the virtuosic talents of James Giles.

"Remembering Lake Michigan" is not meant to evoke so much as to honor my native Chicago. "The Wind Remains" quotes the descending minor third—the "dying fall"—as utilized by Paul Bowles in his little opera (1942) on a Lorca *zarzuela*. And "Remembering Tomorrow" defies explanation, as indeed does any music.

Six Friends

They are: Marian Seldes, the actress; Barbara Grecki, neighbor and confidante; Rosemary and Mary, beloved sister and niece; Don Julien, an intense pal; Jerome Lowenthal, great pianist who just turned seventy-five.

The pieces aren't meant to be portraits so much as modest gifts.

Soundpoints

Here are five small studies composed in Rome in April 2004. They are called "Looking Forward," "Toccata," "Short Bridge," "Another Waltz," and "Looking Back."

They were commissioned by the Walter W. Naumburg Foundation for pianist Gilles Vonsattel.

—Ned Rorem

Recalling was commissioned by the Northwestern University School of Music
for pianist James Giles

First performed 5 May, 2004
at Lutkin Memorial Hall, Northwestern University, Evanston, IL
by James Giles

Recorded by James Giles
on Albany Records TROY 860

Soundpoints was commissioned by the Walter W. Naumburg Foundation

First performed 18 November, 2004, at Alice Tully Hall, NY
by Gilles Vonsattel

CONTENTS

RECALLING
1. Remembering Lake Michigan

NED ROREM

© Copyright 2007 by Boosey & Hawkes Inc.
Copyright for all countries. All rights reserved.

M-051-24639-7

Printed in U.S.A.

Fast, ♩ = 152 (carefully sloppy)

4

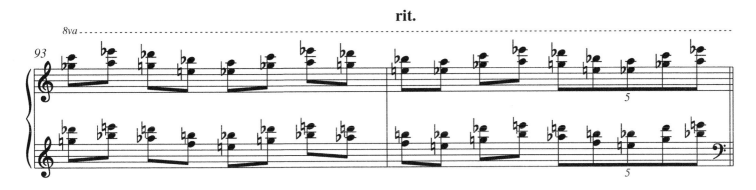

rit.

Tempo I (♩ = 66)

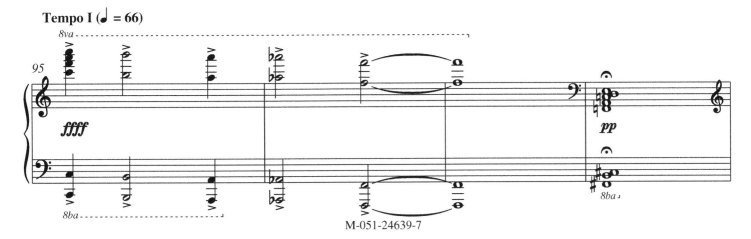

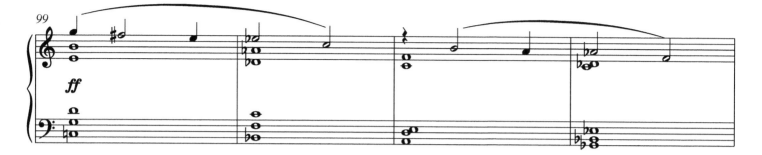

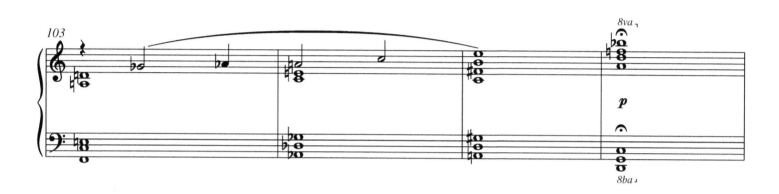

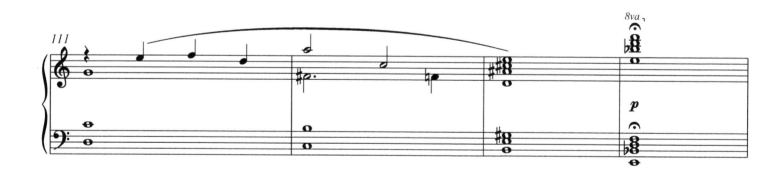

Nantucket
September 2003

2. The Wind Remains
(remembering Paul Bowles)

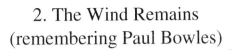

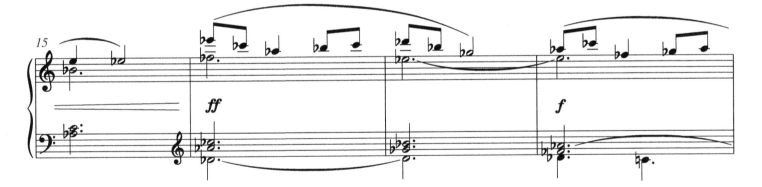

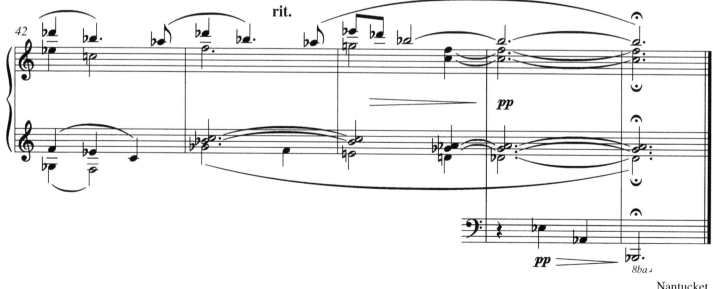

Nantucket
11-13 September 2003

3. Remembering Tomorrow

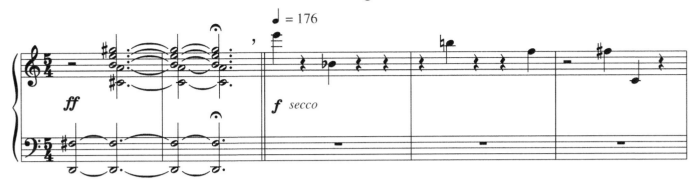

M-051-24639-7

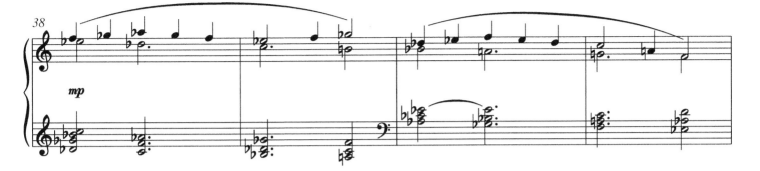

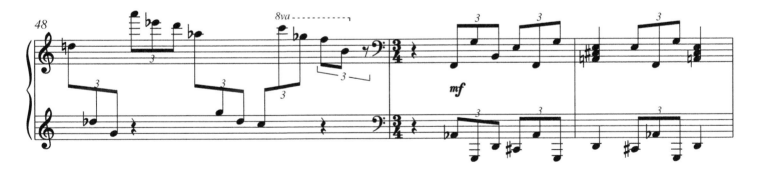

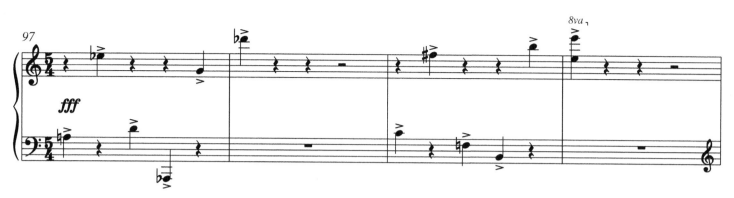

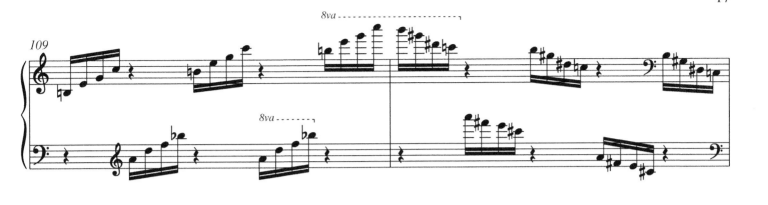

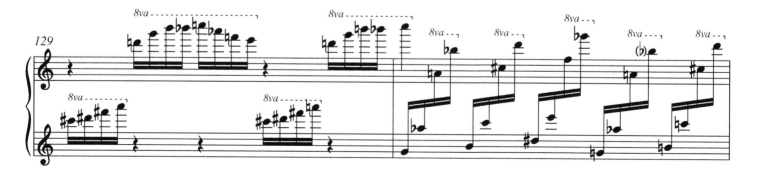

Nantucket
November 2003

SIX FRIENDS

For Marian

NED ROREM

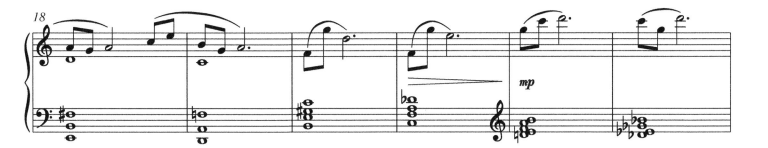

M-051-24639-7

8ba NY
8 April 2006

For Barbara

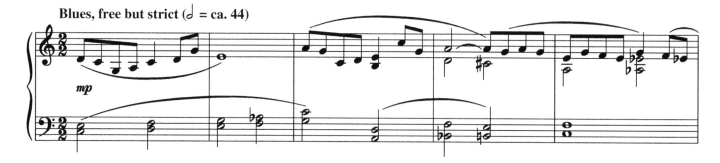

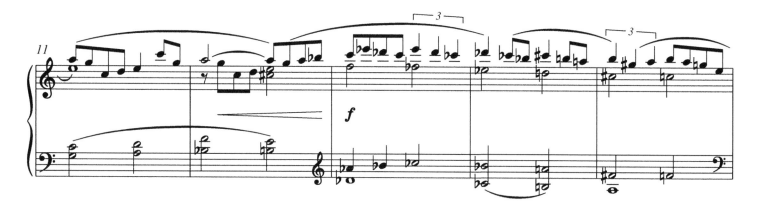

NYC and Nantucket
Sept. 2006

For Rosemary

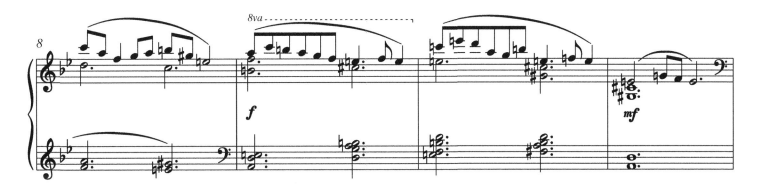

29 Dec. 2006
N.Y.C.

For Mary

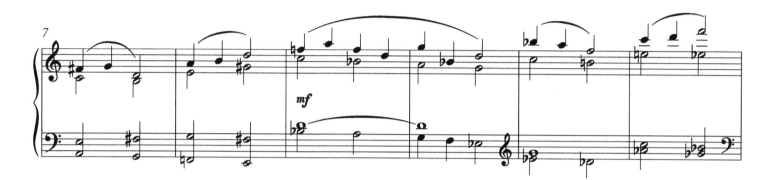

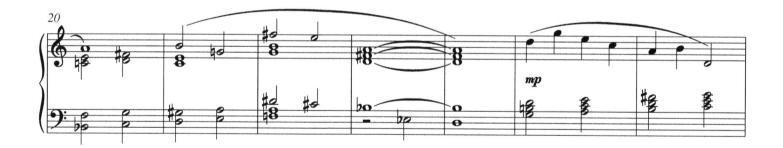

29 Oct. 2006

M-051-24639-7

For Don

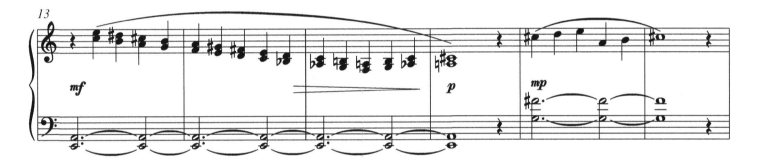

NYC, 15 Sept. 2006

75 Notes for Jerry

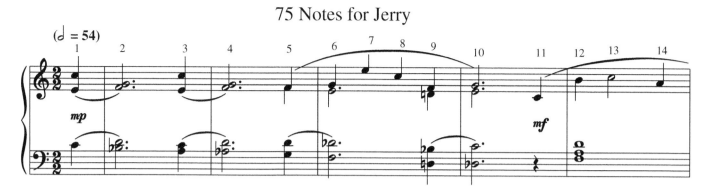

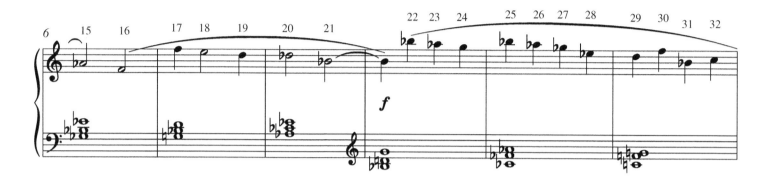

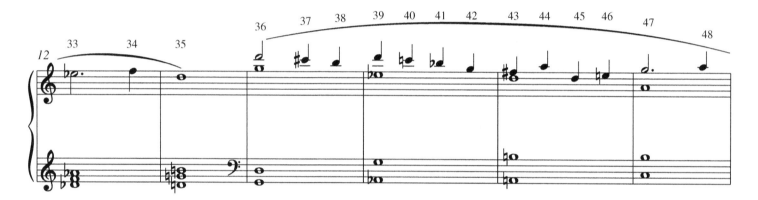

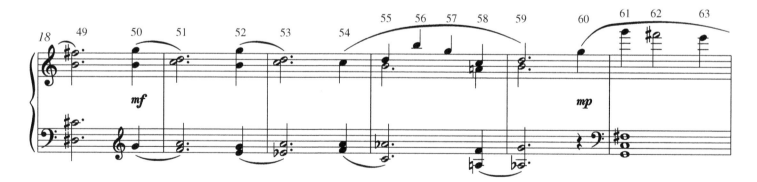

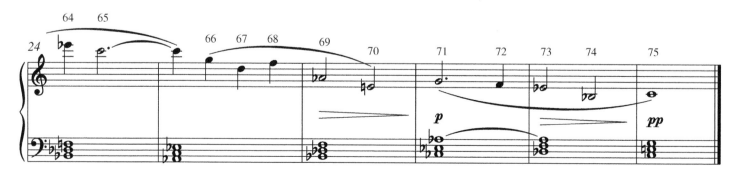

SOUNDPOINTS

1. Looking Forward

NED ROREM

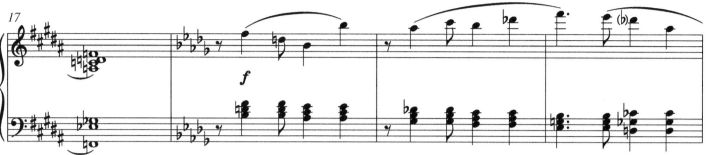

M-051-24639-7

2. Toccata

Very fast

fff *marked and dry*

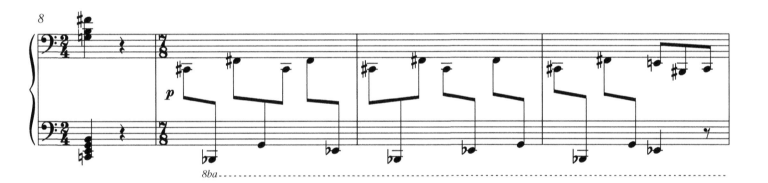

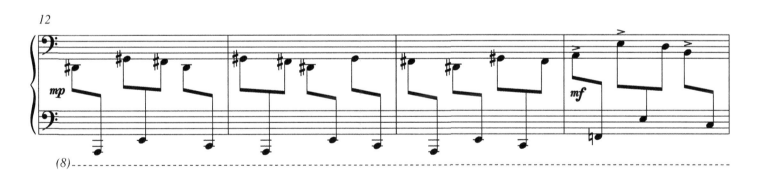

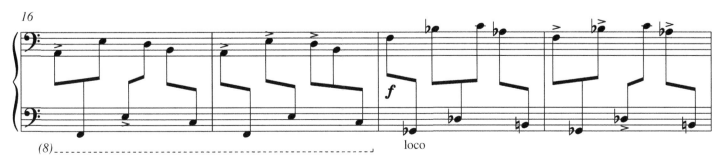

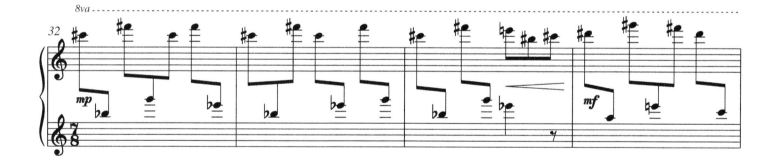

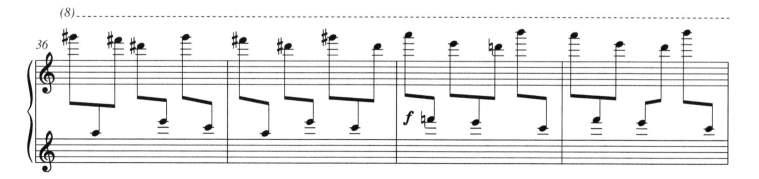

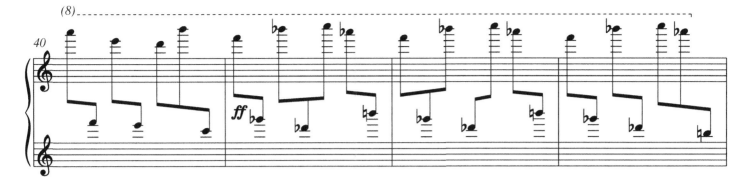

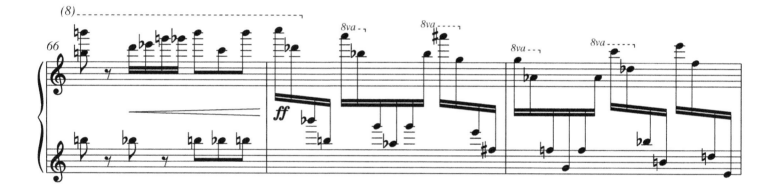

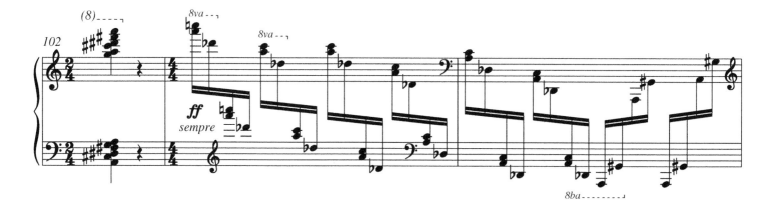

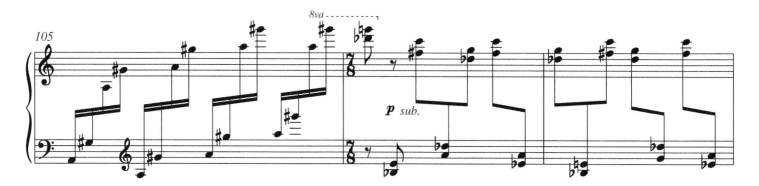

Rome
22 April 2003

3. Short Bridge

4. Another Waltz

17

mp

(L.H. sempre *p*)

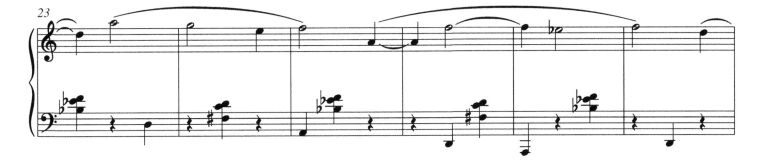

23

29

35

mf

41

38

M-051-24639-7

Rome
25 April 2003

M-051-24639-7

5. Looking Back

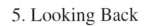

Rome
13 April 2003

M-051-24639-7